AUSTRALIAN BUSH FLOWER REMEDIES

Ian White

This book is dedicated to the memory of the late Edward Bach;
healer and pioneer in the use of Flower Essences.

Revised Editions 1994, 1996, 1998, 2001, 2003

For further information contact

Bush Biotherapies Pty Ltd, trading as Australian Bush Flower Essences

45 Booralie Road, Terrey Hills NSW 2084, Australia

ISBN 0 646 28403 7

Illustrations: Kristin Coburn

Design production: Reno Design, Sydney 18046 / MARCH 2003

Welcome to the AUSTRALIAN BUSH FLOWER REMEDIES, which are catalysts to unlock your full potential, resolve negative beliefs and bring about harmony.

Flower Essences are not something new. The Australian Aborigines have always used them to bring about emotional balance, as did the ancient Egyptians. They were also very popular in the Middle Ages. Paracelsus in the 15th century wrote how he collected the dew from flowering plants and diluted it to treat emotional imbalances. A lot of this knowledge has sadly been lost, although in many cases, such as our Aborigines, this memory has been retained.

Dr Edward Bach rediscovered Flower Essences over fifty years ago using flowers of English plants and shrubs. His vision was that of simplicity. Like Dr Bach, all the great healers such as Hippocrates, Paracelsus, Aristotle and Hahnemann agreed on this point. They believed that good health was the result of emotional, spiritual and mental harmony.

Australian plants have a real beauty and strength. There is something quite remarkable about them. Apart from the fact that Australia has the highest number of flowering plants, they are the oldest in the world. Metaphysically, Australia has always had a very wise, old energy and at the moment there is a tremendous new vitality in this country and New Zealand. This same energy was evident in Greece 2,500 years ago when Hippocrates, Plato and Pythagoras were alive. This energy constantly shifts from country to country, being present in only one country at any particular point in time. It is now here in Australasia. This, combined with the inherent power of the land, manifests in the Australian Bush Flower Essences. They can also be used just as effectively in other countries without losing any of their power.

I grew up in the Australian bush and my father, grandmother, great grandmother and great great grandmother were all herbalists. When I was a young boy, my grandmother would often ask me to accompany her on her trips into the bush. She, like her mother before her, specialised in using and researching the medicinal properties of Australian plants. From her deep understanding she would point out to me the many healing properties of the plants and flowers. I learned a profound respect for nature from her and this was of invaluable assistance to me when I, too, became a practitioner and started working with local plants.

The purpose of the Bush Essences, as I see it, is that they assist in clearing the blocks that stop an individual getting in touch with their true or Higher Self ... their own intuitive part which knows their life purpose.

The Bush Essences not only help to give clarity to one's life purpose but also the courage, strength and enthusiasm to follow and pursue one's goals and dreams. They help to develop a higher level of intuition, self esteem, spirituality, creativity and fun. The Essences also help to resolve any drama and distress in one's life. The more you use the Bush

Essences the more you experience greater clarity and quality in your life. Then everyone benefits … the individual, society and the planet.

The effect of the Essences is similar to that of meditation in that the person accesses the wisdom of their Higher Self. Healing is promoted through the release of negative beliefs and by flooding one's being with the positive virtues (love, joy, faith, courage, etc.) inherent in the Higher Self. When this happens the negative beliefs and thoughts which caused the problem are dissolved and balance is restored.

After my patients have taken these Essences I have seen an obvious and powerful alignment of their personalities and when this happens true wellbeing and harmony occurs.

I am sure the Australian Bush Flower Essences will bring great benefit to you, your patients, family and loved ones.

Sincerely,

IAN WHITE
Naturopath and Homoeopath

ADMINISTERING THE ESSENCES

The Essences work best when either given individually or in a combination addressing the same theme or issue. I feel it is best to take one Essence/combination at a time, except in an acute, one-off situation, ie. when Emergency Essence is needed. The majority of the Essences should be used for two weeks at a time. If, at the end of that period, it appears the Essence has not totally resolved the problem, repeat, or use a different Essence to address the new major issue, if applicable. When taking an Essence, it helps to be aware of its positive virtues as well as the negative emotions it addresses.

The Essences are self adjusting and will release the layers of blocked emotions to whatever 'point of resolution' the person is able to deal with at that point in time.

DOSAGE

Seven (7) drops (from dosage bottle) to be taken, under the tongue, morning and night (on rising and retiring). Take for 14 days unless otherwise specified (they can be taken for longer periods if needed). This dosage is the most effective, easy to remember and builds up a rhythmic healing frequency. If, however, you are intuitively drawn to administer them differently, trust your intuition and follow that.

Combination Essences

This range of Combination Essences, Mists and Creams
is available in leading Natural Health Stores Worldwide.

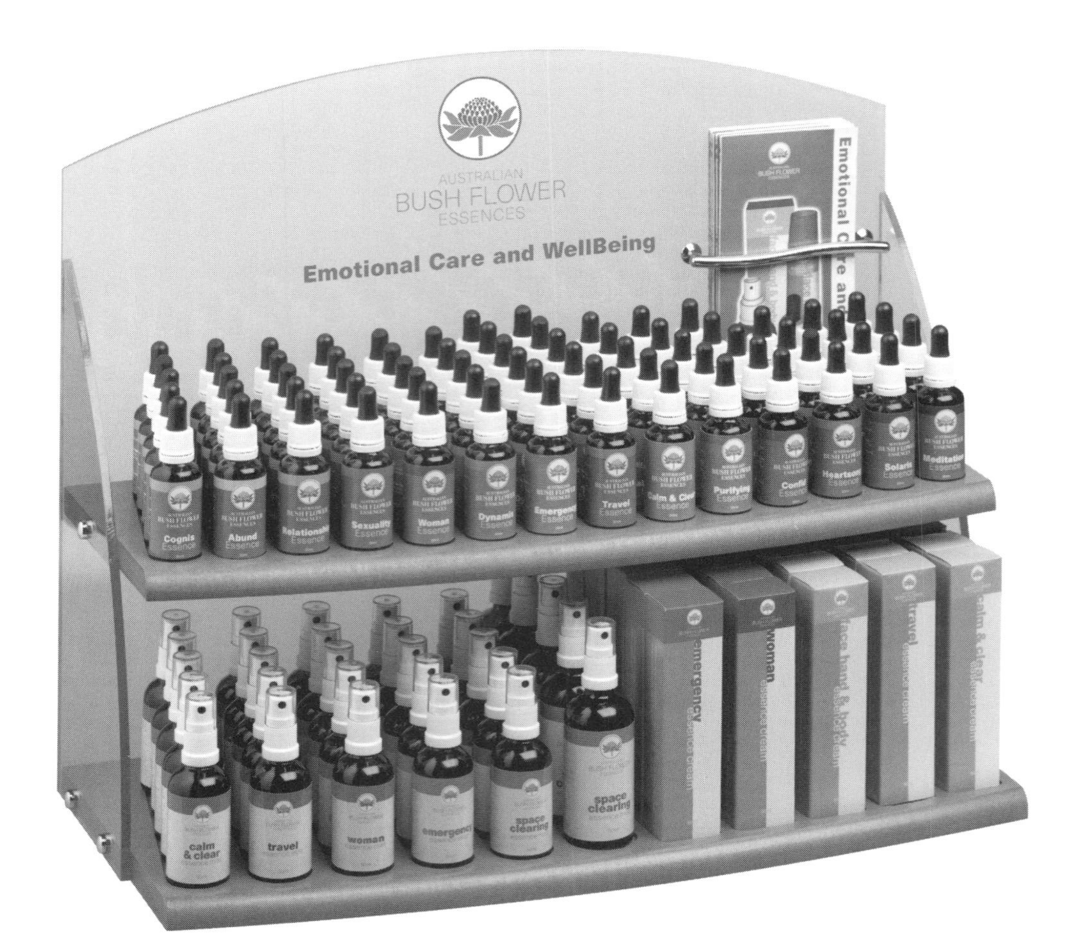

AUSTRALIAN
BUSH FLOWER
ESSENCES
Emotional Care and WellBeing
Cognis
Abund
Relationship
Sexuality
Woman
Dynamis
Emergency
Travel
Calm & Clear
Purifying
Heartsong
Solaris
Meditation
calm & clear
travel
woman
emergency
space clearing
emergency
woman
face hand & body
travel
calm & clear

EMERGENCY ESSENCE

Excellent for any emotional upset. It has a calming effect during a crisis. If a person needs specialised medical help, this Essence will provide comfort until treatment is available. Administer this remedy every hour or more frequently if necessary, until the person feels better.

Bush Flower Essences: Angelsword, Crowea, Dog Rose of the Wild Forces, Fringed Violet, Grey Spider Flower, Sundew and Waratah.
Available in Oral Drops, Mist and Cream.
Slender Rice Flower and Spinifex have also been added to the Cream formulation.

Negative Condition
panic
distress
fear

Positive Outcome
ability to cope

• • •

ABUND ESSENCE

Aids in releasing negative beliefs, family patterns, sabotage and fear of lack. In so doing, it allows you to be open to fully receiving great riches on all levels, not just financial.

Bush Flower Essences: Bluebell, Boab, Christmas Bell, Five Corners, Philotheca, Southern Cross and Sunshine Wattle.
Available in Oral Drops.

Negative Condition
pessimistic
closed to receiving
fear of lack
poverty consciousness

Positive Outcome
joyful sharing
belief in abundance
clears financial sabotage patterns
universal trust

Negative Condition
feeling of hopelessness
insensitive
sense of not belonging
"it's not fair" attitude
embarrassment
rebelliousness
anger

Positive Outcome
coping with change
consideration of others
enhances communication
self esteem

ADOL ESSENCE

This Essence addresses the major issues teenagers commonly experience. It enhances acceptance of self, communication, social skills, harmony in relationships, maturity, emotional stability and optimism.

Bush Flower Essences: Billy Goat Plum, Boab, Bottlebrush, Dagger Hakea, Five Corners, Flannel Flower, Kangaroo Paw, Red Helmet Orchid, Southern Cross, Sunshine Wattle and Tall Yellow Top.
Available in Oral Drops.

•••

Negative Condition
always over committed
no time for self
impatience
rushing
worry

Positive Outcome
encourages own time and space
wind down, relax and have fun
clarity, calmness and peace

CALM AND CLEAR ESSENCE

Helps to find time for one's self, to relax without external pressures and demands, to wind down and enjoy relaxing pursuits.

Bush Flower Essences: Black-eyed Susan, Boronia, Bottlebrush, Bush Fuchsia, Crowea, Jacaranda, Little Flannel Flower and Paw Paw.
Available in Oral Drops, Mist and Cream.

COGNIS ESSENCE

This Essence gives clarity and focus when working, speaking, reading or studying. It balances the intuitive and cognitive processes and helps integrate ideas and information. Excellent for study or pursuits that require intense focus. It assists problem solving by improving access to the Higher Self, which stores all past knowledge and experiences.

Bush Flower Essences: Bush Fuchsia, Isopogon, Jacaranda, Paw Paw and Sundew.
Available in Oral Drops.

Negative Condition
daydreaming
confusion
overwhelm

Positive Outcome
assimilates ideas
clarity and focus
enhances all learning abilities and skills

CONFID ESSENCE

This combination brings out the positive qualities of self esteem and confidence. It allows us to feel comfortable around other people and resolve negative beliefs we may hold about ourselves as well as any guilt we may harbour from past actions. This combination also helps us to take responsibility for situations and events that occur in our lives and realise that we have the ability and power not only to change those events, but also to create those we want.

Bush Flower Essences: Boab, Dog Rose, Five Corners, Southern Cross and Sturt Desert Rose.
Available in Oral Drops.

Negative Condition
low self esteem
guilt
shyness
lack of conviction
victim mentality

Positive Outcome
taking responsibility for one's life
integrity
confidence
personal power
true to one's self

CREATIVE ESSENCE

Negative Condition

creative blocks and inhibitions
difficulty expressing feelings

Positive Outcome

enhances singing
creative expression
clarity of voice
public speaking

Inspires creative and emotional expression and gives courage and clarity in public speaking and singing. This Essence frees the voice. It also helps to clear creative blocks and to find creative solutions in all of life's pursuits.

Bush Flower Essences: Bush Fuchsia, Crowea, Five Corners, Flannel Flower, Red Grevillea, Tall Mulla Mulla and Turkey Bush.
Available in Oral Drops.

• • •

DYNAMIS ESSENCE

Negative Condition

temporary loss of drive, enthusiasm and excitement

Positive Outcome

renews passion and enthusiasm for life

centres and harmonises one's vital forces

Renews enthusiasm and joy for life. It is for those who feel 'not quite right', drained, jaded or not fully recovered from setbacks.

Bush Flower Essences: Banksia Robur, Crowea, Illawarra Flame Tree, Macrocarpa, Old Man Banksia and Yellow Cowslip Orchid.
Available in Oral Drops.

ELECTRO ESSENCE

Greatly relieves fear and distress associated with earth, electrical and electromagnetic radiation. It helps to bring one into balance with the natural rhythms of the earth.

Bush Flower Essences: Bush Fuchsia, Crowea, Fringed Violet, Mulla Mulla, Paw Paw and Waratah.
Available in Oral Drops.

Negative Condition

feeling drained and flat

out of balance with earth rhythms

Positive Outcome

reduces emotional effects of radiation

• • •

FACE, HAND AND BODY ESSENCE

Encourages love, nurturing, care and touch of your physical body. Helps to deal with any dislike and non acceptance of one's body, skin texture or intimate loving touch.

Bush Flower Essences: Billy Goat Plum, Five Corners, Flannel Flower, Little Flannel Flower, Mulla Mulla, She Oak and Wisteria.
Available in Cream.

Negative Condition

dislike of physical self, body, skin texture & touch

Positive Outcome

acceptance of physical body

love & nurturing of self

Negative Condition
poor quality meditation
psychic attack
damaged aura
psychically drained

Positive Outcome
awaken spirituality
enhance intuition
inner guidance
access Higher Self
deeper meditation
telepathy

MEDITATION ESSENCE

This is a wonderful combination to awaken one's spirituality. It allows one to go deeper into any religious or spiritual practice. Enhances access to the Higher Self whilst providing psychic protection and healing of the aura. Highly recommended for anyone practicing meditation.

Bush Flower Essences: Angelsword, Boronia, Bush Fuchsia, Bush Iris, Fringed Violet, Green Spider Orchid and Red Lily.
Available in Oral Drops.

• • •

Negative Condition
emotional waste
feeling encumbered
emotional baggage

Positive Outcome
sense of release and relief
spring cleaned

PURIFYING ESSENCE

To release and clear emotional waste and residual by-products, to clear built-up emotional baggage.

Bush Flower Essences: Bauhinia, Bush Iris, Bottlebrush, Dagger Hakea, Dog Rose and Wild Potato Bush.
Available in Oral Drops.

RELATIONSHIP ESSENCE

Enhances the quality of all relationships, especially intimate ones. It clears and releases resentment, blocked emotions and the confusion, emotional pain and turmoil of a rocky relationship. Helps one verbalise, express feelings and improve communication. This Essence breaks the early negative family conditioning and patterns which effect us in our current adult relationships. For those in intimate relationships a perfect remedy to follow this combination is Sexuality Essence.

Bush Flower Essences: Bluebell, Boab, Bottlebrush, Bush Gardenia, Dagger Hakea, Flannel Flower, Mint Bush, Red Helmet Orchid, Red Suva Frangipani and Wedding Bush.
Available in Oral Drops.

Negative Condition
emotional pain and turmoil
confusion
resentment
blocked, held in emotions
inability to relate

Positive Outcome
expressing feelings
enhanced communication
forgiveness
breaks negative family conditioning
renews interest
enhances parental-child bonding

•••

SENSUALITY ESSENCE

Encourages the ability to enjoy physical and emotional intimacy, passion and sensual fulfilment.

Bush Flower Essences: Billy Goat Plum, Bush Gardenia, Flannel Flower, Little Flannel Flower, Macrocarpa and Wisteria.
Available in Mist.

Negative Condition
Fear of emotional and physical intimacy

Positive Outcome
encourages intimacy, passion and sensual fulfilment

Negative Condition

effects of sexual abuse
shame
uptight about sexuality
fear of intimacy

Positive Outcome

renews passion
sensuality
enjoy touch and intimacy
playfullness
fulfilment

SEXUALITY ESSENCE

This Essence is helpful for releasing shame and the effects of physical or sexual abuse and trauma. It allows one to feel comfortable with and to fully accept one's body. It enables the individual to be open to sensuality and touch and to enjoy physical and emotional intimacy.
Sexuality Essence renews passion and interest in relationships.

Bush Flower Essences: Billy Goat Plum, Bush Gardenia, Flannel Flower, Fringed Violet, Little Flannel Flower, Sturt Desert Rose and Wisteria.
Available in Oral Drops.

• • •

Negative Condition

fear and distress
associated with fire

Positive Outcome

reduces the negative effects
of fire and the sun's rays

SOLARIS ESSENCE

Greatly relieves fear and distress associated with fire, heat and sun. An excellent remedy to have handy during summer and long exposure to the sun.

Bush Flower Essences: Mulla Mulla, She Oak and Spinifex.
Available in Oral Drops.

SPACE CLEARING ESSENCE

Creates sacred, safe and harmonious environments. Purifies and releases enviroments of built up negative emotional, mental and psychic energies. Great for clearing tense situations and environments and restoring balance.

Bush Flower Essences: Angelsword, Boab, Fringed Violet, Lichen and Red Lily.
Available in Mist.

Negative Condition

negative mental, emotional and psychic energies

disharmonious or unpleasant environments

Positive Outcome

enhances sacred space

clears negative and psychic energies

creates safe, harmonious environments

allows one to feel still and reflective

• • •

TRANSITION ESSENCE

This combination helps one to cope and move through any major life change. It brings about an awareness of one's life direction especially for people who are at a crossroad. Alternatively those who know what they want but do not know how to achieve it will benefit from this combination. It also eases the fear of death as well as helping one come to terms with it. This remedy, consequently, allows one to easily and gently pass over with calmness, dignity and serenity.

Bush Flower Essences: Autumn Leaves, Bauhinia, Bottlebrush, Bush Iris, Lichen, Mint Bush, Red Grevillea and Silver Princess.
Available in Oral Drops.

Negative Condition

feeling stuck

lack of direction

fear of death

fear of the unknown

non-acceptance

Positive Outcome

acceptance of change

serenity

eases fear of death

passing over in peace

Negative Condition

disorientation

personally depleted and drained

emotional effects of travel

Positive Outcome

refreshes

centres

maintains sense of personal space

• • •

Negative Condition

mood swings

weary

physical dislike

Positive Outcome

female balance

calms and stabilises

coping with change

TRAVEL ESSENCE

This combination particularly addresses the problems encountered with jet travel. It enables a person to arrive at their destination feeling balanced and ready to go. The use of this Essence is beneficial for all forms of travel.

Bush Flower Essences: Banksia Robur, Bottlebrush, Bush Fuchsia, Bush Iris, Crowea, Fringed Violet, Macrocarpa, Mulla Mulla, Paw Paw, Red Lily, She Oak, Silver Princess, Sundew and Tall Mulla Mulla.
Available in Oral Drops, Mist and Cream.

WOMAN ESSENCE

Harmonises any imbalances during menstruation and menopause.
It allows a woman to discover and feel good about herself, her own body and her beauty.

Bush Flower Essences: Billy Goat Plum, Bottlebrush, Bush Fuchsia, Crowea, Five Corners, Mulla Mulla, Old Man Banksia, Peach-flowered Tea-tree and She Oak.
Available in Oral Drops, Mist and Cream.

Individual Essences

These essences come individually or in a Stock Kit.

AUSTRALIAN
BUSH FLOWER
ESSENCES
Turkey Bush
Waratah
Wedding Bush

Alpine Mint Bush

Prostanthera cuneata

Negative Condition

mental & emotional exhaustion

•

lack of joy and weight of responsibility of care givers

Positive Outcome

revitalisation

•

joy

•

renewal

This flower grows in exposed rocky sites in the alpine and sub-alpine areas of south eastern Australia. This Essence works on the mental and emotional levels. It is for people who work in healing, health administration and caring situations where there is a great deal of responsibility for other people. They give much of themselves both physically and emotionally, often listening to people in pain and need. These care givers can be in danger of burning out or becoming disillusioned. They can reach a point of tiredness feeling their life has lost its joy. Alpine Mint Bush can revitalise and bring about in these people a renewed enthusiasm and joy in their life for what they do.

Angelsword

Lobelia gibbosa

Negative Condition

interference with true spiritual connection to Higher Self

•

spiritually possessed

•

spiritual confusion

Positive Outcome

spiritual discernment

•

accessing gifts from past lifetimes

•

release of negatively held psychic energies

•

clear spiritual communication

This amazing flower grows in the alpine region of Australia. Viewed from one angle, it has the appearance of a 'fleur-de-lis'. The Essence is for reaching one's own spiritual truth by cutting through any confusion or misinformation, ie. helping one discern the level of truth in 'channelled messages'. When the flower is looked at the opposite way, it resembles a monk in purple robes accentuated by the yellow stamens at the third eye. Taking this Essence allows access and retrieval of previously developed gifts from past lives. Angelsword protects from outside influences and entities so one can receive clear information from one's Higher Self without interference. Whilst Fringed Violet works to repair damage to the aura, Angelsword releases any energies that entered while the aura was open.

Banksia Robur

Banksia robur

Negative Condition

disheartened
•
lethargic
•
frustrated

Positive Outcome

enjoyment of life
•
enthusiasm
•
interest in life

Banksia Robur is commonly known as Swamp Banksia as it is usually found by creek banks. This Essence addresses temporary loss of drive and enthusiasm due to burn out, disappointment or frustration. It is different to Old Man Banksia as it is for people who are normally very dynamic. It will pick them up out of the 'bog' they are in and get them back on solid ground and going again. When bathing add seven drops of this Essence to the bath which will enhance the effect of the remedy as it will assist in washing away negativity.

Bauhinia

Lysiphyllum cunninghamii

Negative Condition

resistance to change

•

rigidity

•

reluctance

Positive Outcome

acceptance

•

open mindedness

Made up near Geikie Gorge in the Kimberleys, this Essence is for embracing new concepts and ideas. There may be some hesitation or reluctance, initially, in coming to terms with these. It can even help when there is a person who is annoying you or whom you dislike. For example, a family of a different nationality may become neighbours and even though you may not be racist, you may have difficulty in accepting their different manners and customs. This remedy is also good for older people who are very set in their ways.

Billy Goat Plum

Planchonia careya

Negative Condition

shame
•
inability to accept
the physical self
•
physical loathing

Positive Outcome

sexual pleasure and enjoyment
•
acceptance of self
and one's physical body
•
openmindedness

For feelings of shame, self disgust and self loathing. For those people who feel revolted and dirty about sex and feel unclean afterwards. It can also be for feelings of revulsion about other physical aspects such as acne, eczema, a large nose, etc.

Black-eyed Susan

Tetratheca ericifolia

Negative Condition

impatience
•
'on the go'
•
over committed
•
constant striving

Positive Outcome

ability to turn inward and be still
•
slowing down
•
inner peace

For people who are impatient or always 'on the go'. These people are continually rushing and their lives are always overflowing with commitments. This Essence enables these people to slow down, to reach that still centre within and find calmness and inner guidance.

Bluebell

Wahlenbergia species

Made in the Olgas, one of the main spiritual centres in Australia, this Essence helps to open the heart. It is for those who feel cut off from their feelings. The emotion is there, but is held within. They are subconsciously afraid to express it for they fear their feelings of love, joy, etc. are finite or not renewable. They operate from a subconscious fear that there is just not enough and that if they let go of what they have, they will not survive. This fear can often be marked by a controlling, rigid and forthright manner.

Negative Condition

closed
•
fear of lack
•
greed
•
rigidity

Positive Outcome

opens the heart
•
belief in abundance
•
universal trust
•
joyful sharing
•
unconditional love

Boab

Adansonia gibbosa

Negative Condition

enmeshment in negative
family patterns
•
for recipients of abuse
and prejudice

Positive Outcome

personal freedom by
releasing family patterns
•
clearing of other, non-family,
negative Karmic connections

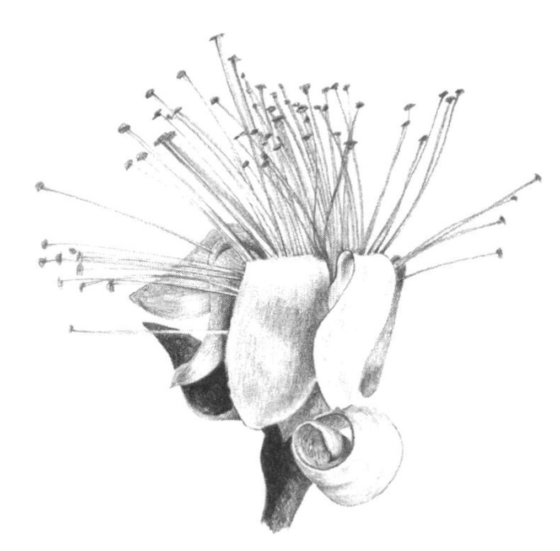

The Boab tree is found only in the Kimberley region of north west Australia. This is one of the most powerful of all the Bush Essences and has brought about profound change. Boab clears negative emotional and mental family patterns that are passed on from generation to generation. Boab can access and clear those core patterns and all the related ensuing beliefs. This Essence is very beneficial in helping those who have had experiences of abuse or prejudice from others.
Boab will also help clear the negative lines of karma between people. When used in a spray it can be very effective in clearing negative energies, especially when combined with Fringed Violet, Angelsword and Lichen. Boab can help break the chains that have been around human consciousness for thousands of years.

Boronia

Boronia ledifolia

Negative Condition

obsessive thoughts
•
pining
•
broken hearted

Positive Outcome

clarity
•
serenity
•
creative visualisation

This is the Essence for resolving obsessions — thoughts, events, things or ideas which are stuck. It leads to clarity and focus. It combines wonderfully with Bottlebrush for breaking habits and addictions and for dealing with an ended relationship when there is pining for the other person. It also enhances focus for creative visualisation.

Bottlebrush

Callistemon linearis

Negative Condition

unresolved mother issues

•

overwhelmed by major life changes — old age, adolescence, parenthood, pregnancy, approaching death

Positive Outcome

serenity and calm

•

ability to cope and move on

•

mother-child bonding

This Essence helps people move through major life changes and the overwhelm that often goes with those changes, especially retirement, menopause, adolescence or death, etc. It 'brushes' out the past and allows the person to move on. An excellent remedy for pregnant women and new mothers who feel inadequate. It will help throughout pregnancy until after the birth and will assist with bonding between the mother and child. It is excellent for healing unresolved mother issues.

Bush Fuchsia

Epacris longiflora

Negative Condition

switched off

•

nervousness about public speaking

•

ignoring 'gut' feelings

•

clumsy

Positive Outcome

courage to speak out

•

clarity

•

in touch with intuition

•

integration of information

•

integration of male and female aspects

This Essence assists with problem solving and improves one's access to intuition — it helps a person to trust their own 'gut' feelings. It allows for balance between the logical/rational and the intuitive/creative, ie. the integration between the male and female aspects. It will give people courage and clarity in public speaking as well as the ability to speak out about their own convictions.

Bush Gardenia

Gardenia megasperma

Negative Condition

stale relationships
•
self interest
•
unaware

Positive Outcome

passion
•
renews interest in partner
•
improves communication

For renewing passion and interest in relationships. It helps draw together those who are moving away from one another, busy in their own world (career, life, etc.). It is as if this Essence helps to turn the individual's head to reconnect to see what their partner is doing and feeling and to discover what is needed to bring them back together.

It is not only for male/female relationships but also for family relationships. This flower has similar flowers and scent to that of the suburban garden shrub but is a 40 ft tree, growing in the tropical north, similar in shape to a Eucalypt.

Bush Iris

Patersonia longifolia

Negative Condition

fear of death
•
materialism
•
atheism
•
physical excess
•
avarice

Positive Outcome

awakening of spirituality
•
acceptance of death
as a transition state
•
clearing blocks in the
base chakra and trust centre

This was one of the first Essences to be prepared. It is an Essence to open people up to their spirituality and to access the doorway to their higher perceptions. It allows the trinity to flow into a person and is an excellent remedy to give someone who has just started meditation or 'conscious' spiritual growth. In the negative mode there will be materialism and/or atheism. There may also be a deep seated fear of death.

Crowea

Crowea saligna

Negative Condition

continual worrying

•

a sense of being
'not quite right'

Positive Outcome

peace and calm

•

balances and centres
the individual

•

clarity of one's feelings

For people who are feeling 'not quite right' with themselves and are just a little out of balance. An excellent Essence for people not sure of what it is they are feeling. It is great for worry and distress. It is for those who always have something to worry about without having specific fears. This purple flower has five petals with a prominent raised centre. Five in numerology relates to the emotional centre and the integration of emotions.

Dagger Hakea

Hakea teretifolia

Negative Condition

resentment

•

bitterness towards
close family, friends, lovers

Positive Outcome

forgiveness

•

open expression of feelings

For people who feel resentment and bitterness and hold grudges against those with whom they have been very close, eg. family members and old lovers. This resentment is often not openly displayed. The plant gets its name from the needle-like barb that grows on its leaves.

Dog Rose

Bauera rubioides

Negative Condition

fearful
•
shy
•
insecure
•
apprehensive
with other people
•
niggling fears

Positive Outcome

confidence
•
belief in self
•
courage
•
ability to embrace life
more fully

The striking feature of Dog Rose is that the flowers hang down and appear to have dropped and rounded shoulders, like a defeated person. Dog Rose is the Essence for treating fears, niggling little fears, not terror. Overcoming fear allows an increase in the flow of the vital force, quality of life, courage and self esteem. It is also for shy, insecure, timid, nervous people.

Dog Rose of the Wild Forces

Bauera sessiliflora

Found only in Victoria, this Essence was made up from a plant quivering and leaning over the surging white water just below Mackenzie Falls, in Gariwerd, (previously known as The Grampians). This plant is commonly found growing close to the water and, like Dog Rose, it deals with fear. It is taken when a person has a fear of losing control, when the emotions they are feeling within themselves or immediately around them are just so intense there is a sense of losing total control. On a higher level it helps to teach the necessity of gaining control over the emotions so that emotional intensity will not distort one's natural energies.

Negative Condition

fear of losing control

•

hysteria

•

pain with no apparent cause

Positive Outcome

calm and centred
in times of inner and
outer turmoil

•

emotional balance

Five Corners

Styphelia triflora

Negative Condition

low self esteem
•
dislike of self
•
crushed, held in personality
•
clothing drab and colourless

Positive Outcome

love and acceptance of self
•
celebration of own beauty
•
joyousness

This tall, proud shrub gets its name from its fruit which has five corners. Five Corners corresponds with the anatomical position of arms and legs spread with the fifth point being the head. This Essence allows the life force to flow through to these five centres. When this happens a person feels good and strong in themselves. They feel their own love and beauty. The Essence resolves low self esteem, lack of confidence and diminished self love. In the negative mode the person will appear crushed and 'held in'.

Flannel Flower

Actinotus helianthi

Negative Condition

dislike of being touched
•
lack of sensitivity in males
•
uncomfortable with intimacy

Positive Outcome

gentleness and sensitivity in touching
•
trust
•
openness
•
expression of feelings
•
joy in physical activity

The petals of this flower resemble the sensuous texture of flannel — it almost begs to be touched and felt. This Essence is for people who are uncomfortable with emotional intimacy as well as physical contact and touching. They often have difficulty in maintaining their personal boundaries. It helps one to totally trust and express verbally their innermost feelings. It brings to both males and females a desire to and enjoyment in, expressing themselves physically. It is excellent for males allowing for a gentleness, softness and sensitivity in touching.

Freshwater Mangrove

Barringtonia acutangula

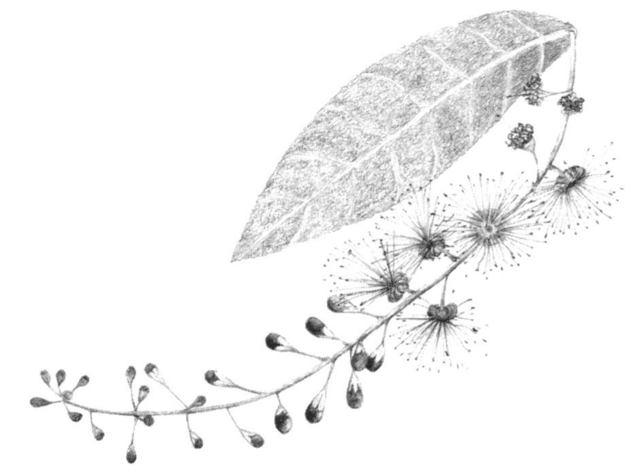

Negative Condition

heart closed due to
expectations or prejudices
which have been taught,
not personally experienced

Positive Outcome

openness to new experiences,
people and perceptual shifts
•
healthy questioning
of traditional standards
and beliefs

This flowering tree grows beside fresh water creeks, billabongs and swamps in the Northern Territory. The healing quality of the Essence is to release and heal mental prejudice, allowing the heart to open without prejudgement. The prejudice of Slender Rice Flower stems from direct personal experience whereas Freshwater Mangrove is for those who mentally reject or have already made up their mind about something without it ever being experienced. Often the seeds of this prejudice have been sown for a long time. In many cases it is generational, as in the case of countries where religious prejudice is passed on and accepted by the young without question. Many prejudices are built because of cultural or societal belief that something cannot be done. This Essence has the potential to allow us to fully experience and be open on both a mental and heart level to new perceptual shifts and all the changes occurring at this time.

Fringed Violet

Thysanotus tuberosus

Negative Condition

damage to aura

•

distress

•

lack of psychic protection

Positive Outcome

removal of effects of
recent or old distressing events

•

heals damage to aura

•

psychic protection

For treating damage to the aura where there has been shock, grief or distress e.g. from abuse or assault. This remedy maintains psychic protection and is excellent for people who are drained by others or those who unconsciously absorb the physical and emotional imbalances of others. It releases shock from the body. When used in combination with Flannel Flower or Wisteria it is beneficial for those who have suffered abuse.

Green Spider Orchid

Caladenia dilatata

Negative Condition

nightmares and phobias
from past life experiences
•
intense negative reactions
to the sight of blood

Positive Outcome

telepathic communication
•
ability to withhold information
until timing is appropriate
•
attunement

This remedy was also made up in Gariwerd (The Grampians) Victoria and is very much aligned with higher learnings, philosophies and deeper insight. This Essence can assist in working with telepathy, to attune a person to be more receptive to not only other people but also other species and kingdoms. It is for people who are teaching spiritual matters and understandings, helping them to impart that knowledge. It helps us to know when to share about our spiritual experiences, ideas before they are manifested and incomplete projects and when to remain silent to let the energy build. Green Spider Orchid can release nightmares, terror and phobias stemming from past lives.

Grey Spider Flower

Grevillea buxifolia

Negative Condition

terror
•
fear of supernatural and psychic attack

Positive Outcome

faith
•
calm
•
courage

This is an Essence to deal with extreme terror, especially terror experienced in life-threatening situations or psychic attack. It deals with panic and nightmares. The Essence will restore faith and trust. Interestingly enough every time I picked this flower to make the Essence I came across a spider. There is a theory that spiders are an archetypal image for primordial fear.

Gymea Lily

Doryanthes excelsa

Negative Condition

arrogant
•
attention seeking
•
craving status and glamour
•
dominating and
over-riding personality

Positive Outcome

humility
•
allowing others to express
themselves and contribute
•
awareness, appreciation
and taking notice of others

Also known as the Giant Lily, this extraordinary plant bears large red flowers on a huge terminal head atop a stem of up to four metres high. Being so high the flowers are not seen clearly from the ground. This remedy is for excessive pride and arrogance and helps bring about humility. The Essence is for reaching up to the energy of arrogance and transforming it to achieve great heights. It gives strength to those who are ahead of their peers and helps them to stay at the top. Gymea Lily is also very beneficial for people whose personalities are very intense or extrovert, or those who are dominating, demanding and very charismatic who usually get their way. It is also for people who like to be seen and noticed and who seek glamour and status.

Hibbertia

Hibbertia penduculata

Negative Condition

fanatical about
self improvement

•

driven to acquire knowledge

•

excessive self discipline

•

superiority

Positive Outcome

content with own
knowledge

•

acceptance

•

ownership and utilitisation
of own knowledge

For people who are strict and regimented or even fanatical with themselves or for those who use their knowledge to gain an upper hand. They constantly devour information and philosophies purely to make themselves better people but often without truly integrating it. In the positive mode these people will be accepting of themselves and their own innate knowledge and experiences, without wanting to be superior to others.

Illawarra Flame Tree

Brachychiton acerifolius

Negative Condition

overwhelming sense of rejection
•
fear of responsibility

Positive Outcome

confidence
•
commitment
•
self reliance
•
self approval

An Essence for those who suffer from a great sense of rejection, or who feel 'left out'. This rejection is deeply felt and is very agonising for the person. The Essence is also for self rejection, or for a person feeling apprehensive about a new experience, eg. parenthood, or where there is a fear of responsibility. This Essence will help a person take that first step. It is also beneficial for those whose numbers in numerology are 11, 22 or 33 — people who have usually chosen to do very important work this life.

Isopogon

Isopogon anethifolius

Negative Condition

inability to learn from past experience
•
stubborn
•
controlling personality

Positive Outcome

ability to learn from past experience
•
retrieval of forgotten skills
•
relating without manipulating or controlling
•
ability to remember the past

This Essence is for those who live very much in their heads. They are dominated by their intellect and there is often a separation between their heart and head. This Essence, like Tall Yellow Top, connects the heart and the head. It especially benefits those people who control through stubbornness. It also enables the retrieval of long-forgotten skills and information.

The small spiral arrangement of this plant's yellow flowers fade and leave a small, grey, round nut which will stay on the plant for many years. In spiritual symbolism the colour yellow represents wisdom and knowledge.

Jacaranda

Jacaranda mimosaefolia

Negative Condition

scattered
•
changeable
•
dithering
•
rushing

Positive Outcome

decisiveness
•
quick thinking
•
centred

An Essence for people who dither, never completing things because they are constantly changing them. There is a fine distinction between Sundew and Jacaranda. Sundew deals with dreamers (the 'space cadet'), whilst Jacaranda is for those who dither, are 'all over the place' and are always changing their mind.

Kangaroo Paw

Anigozanthos manglesii

Negative Condition

gauche
•
unaware
•
insensitive
•
inept
•
clumsy

Positive Outcome

kindness
•
sensitivity
•
savoire faire
•
enjoyment of people
•
relaxed

This Essence is for people who are 'green' and socially inept. They do not know how to properly interact with other people. They can be very insensitive because they are so focused on themselves that they miss the cues and needs of other people around them. They can be very self centred.

Kapok Bush

Cochlospermum fraseri

Negative Condition

apathy
•
resignation
•
discouraged
•
half hearted

Positive Outcome

willingness
•
application
•
'give it a go'
•
persistence
•
perception

Mount Barnett, an Aboriginal Cattle Station on the rugged Gibb River Road in the Kimberleys, was where I made this Essence.
It is for people who have a tendency to give up very easily, who are easily discouraged. It can also give people an overview of a plan or situation and then allow them to work it through sequentially and be able to bring it to fruition. It could even be for someone with a piece of technology or machinery, to assist them to understand how it works.

Little Flannel Flower

Actinotus minor

Negative Condition

denial of the 'child' within
•
seriousness in children
•
grimness in adults

Positive Outcome

care free
•
playfulness
•
joyful

This Essence deals with the child aspect in us all. It addresses the expression of playfulness, being carefree and spontaneous joy. It is for people who regard life as a very sombre and serious experience. It is also for children who tend to grow up much too quickly, who take on the troubles of the world and get old before their time. It helps children get in contact with their spirit guides. Its delicate, tiny, white flowers cover the bush with a blanket of colour and white light, yet it is easily overlooked due to its size.

Macrocarpa

Eucalyptus macrocarpa

Negative Condition

drained
•
jaded
•
worn out

Positive Outcome

enthusiasm
•
inner strength
•
endurance

Macrocarpa is a Eucalypt that grows in the wheat belt area of south west Western Australia, the stands of which are becoming increasingly rare and very few survive today. This tree has the largest flower of any Eucalypt. Both the tree and the flower have a tremendous power about them and this comes out in its properties. This Essence brings about renewed enthusiasm, endurance and inner strength.

Mint Bush

Prostanthera striatiflora

Negative Condition

perturbation
•
confusion
•
spiritual emergence
•
initial turmoil and
void of spiritual initiation

Positive Outcome

smooth spiritual initiation
•
clarity
•
calmness
•
ability to cope

This Essence like many others, was made in the Valley of the Winds in the Olgas (or Katajuta) in central Australia. Mint Bush helps one to cope with the dross being burnt off before emerging at a new spiritual level. Just prior to any such initiation there are usually spiritual trials and tribulations that one goes through when one feels they are being tested, often to their limit. At this time there is usually a great deal of confusion and one can have a sense that everything is too difficult and too much to deal with and resolve. These feelings can also arise during intense changes in your life — divorce, bankruptcy, severe illness or accidents, changing religious beliefs or affiliations.

Mountain Devil

Lambertia formosa

Negative Condition

hatred
•
anger
•
holding grudges
•
suspiciousness

Positive Outcome

unconditional love
•
happiness
•
healthy boundaries
•
forgiveness

This Essence helps one deal with feelings of hatred, anger, jealousy and the major blocks to expressing love. It is for people who tend to be suspicious of others. Mountain Devil helps to develop unconditional love and acceptance. It helps one express anger in a healthy way and so develop sound boundaries. This may open the way to forgiveness.

Mulla Mulla

Ptilotus atripicifolius

Negative Condition

fear of flames
and hot objects
•
distress associated with
exposure to heat and sun

Positive Outcome

reduces the effects
of fire and sun
•
feeling comfortable
with fire and heat

Mulla Mulla is for the personal recovery from the shattering experience of burns from heat or fire. This Essence reduces the negative effects of fire and the sun's rays. It is for those with a fear of fire or flames (often from a past life). If this fear is unconscious it will often manifest in a lack of vitality, as if they wish to fade away. If a person presents with this picture they can, with appropriate counselling, reveal this fear of fire or hot objects. This Essence was made up in Palm Valley, one of the hottest parts of the country and where some of the oldest plants in Australia are found.

Old Man Banksia

Banksia serrata

Negative Condition

weary
•
phlegmatic personalities
•
disheartened
•
frustrated

Positive Outcome

enjoyment of life
•
renews enthusiasm
•
interest in life

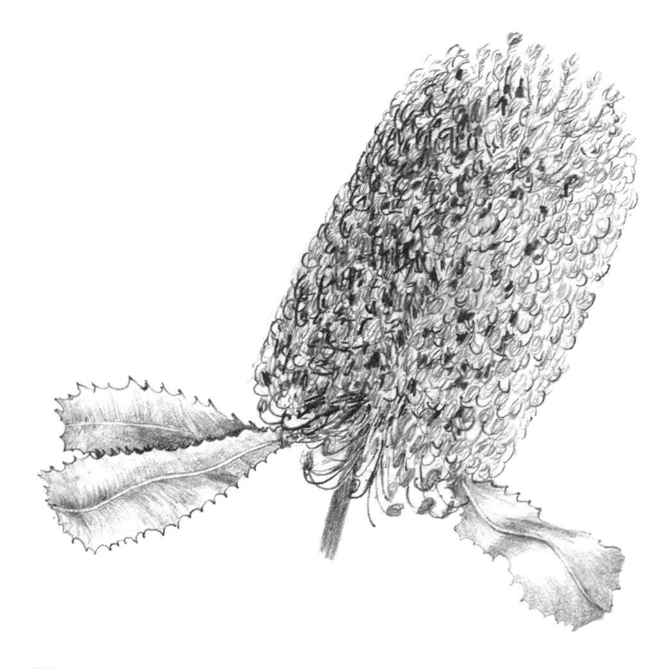

For people who are weary, frustrated and disheartened by setbacks. This Essence helps to bring a spark into those people's lives who are heavy and slow moving. They tend to be reliable, dependable people who steadily plod on, often hiding their weariness while battling on with unceasing effort. The Old Man Banksia is a gnarled and twisted tree and it seems to be a storehouse of old wisdom. It is one of the first plants discovered by Joseph Banks.

Paw Paw

Carica papaya

Negative Condition

overwhelm
•
unable to resolve problems
•
burdened by decision

Positive Outcome

improved access to
Higher Self for problem solving
•
assimilation of new ideas
•
calmness
•
clarity

For the assimilation and integration of new ideas and information, especially where there is a tendency to feel overwhelmed by the quality and quantity of that information. A feature of this plant is its very narrow stem which, at the top, branches into a mass of foliage to bear large and ponderous fruits. This Essence should be used when one is unable to solve a problem. It will activate the Higher Self, where we have the answer to all our problems. It will ease the burden of problems as it activates the intuitive processes to provide solutions.

Peach-flowered Tea-tree

Leptospermum squarrosum

Negative Condition

mood swings
•
lack of commitment to follow through projects
•
easily bored
•
hypochondriacs

Positive Outcome

ability to complete projects
•
personal stability
•
take responsibility for one's health

This is an Essence for people with extreme mood swings, hypochondriacal people and especially those who have a fear of getting old. It can also be used for people who get enthusiastic and then, for no apparent reason, lose that enthusiasm. It is for those who do not 'follow through' on their goals and convictions. Once the challenge goes they become bored and lose interest. It will help develop stability, consistency, drive and commitment.

Philotheca

Philotheca salsolifolia

Negative Condition

inability to accept acknowledgement

•

excessive generosity

Positive Outcome

ability to receive love and acknowledgement

•

ability to let in praise

This Essence allows people to accept acknowledgement for their achievements and to 'let in' love. They are often good listeners and generous, giving people. It allows shy people to speak of their plans and success. In its natural environment, the flower is easily overlooked and often mistaken for other species.

Pink Mulla Mulla

Ptilotus helipteroides

Negative Condition

deep ancient wound
on the psyche
•
an outer guarded
and prickly persona to prevent
being hurt
•
keeps people at a distance

Positive Outcome

deep spiritual healing
•
trusting and opening up

This annual is found in the stony country of the outback and has a striking, pinky-purple conical flower head. The Pink Mulla Mulla is for those who have suffered a deep spiritual wound long ago, often in their first incarnation, where they felt abandoned by Spirit which has led to a deep scar on the soul and psyche. It works on the outer causal bodies clearing sabotage (and fear of spiritual abandonment once more) that is stopping their spiritual growth. On an emotional level, Pink Mulla Mulla is for those who put out prickles to keep people away. They tend to be quite isolated and unable to resolve a hurt, wrong or injustice which can be felt very deeply. This impinges on their attitude to those around them and can make them suspicious of people's motives, allowing them no rest. They are often on guard against people hurting them again, they may protect themselves by saying hurtful things to others. What they say to those around them does not always reflect how they really feel. It is merely a way of keeping people at a safe distance.

Red Grevillea

Grevillea speciosa

Negative Condition

feeling stuck
•
oversensitive
•
affected by criticism
and unpleasant people
•
too reliant on others

Positive Outcome

boldness
•
strength to leave
unpleasant situations
•
indifference to the
judgement of others

This Essence is for people who feel stuck. It acts as a catalyst for those who know what they want to achieve but do not know how to go about it. It is for people who are too reliant on others. It promotes independence and boldness. This Essence is extremely effective though the changes may not be as anticipated. Like the Grey Spider Flower this plant is a member of the Grevillea family and its flowers are a dark red colour, similar in colour to the Waratah.

Red Helmet Orchid

Corybas dilatatus

Negative Condition

rebelliousness
•
hot-headed
•
unresolved father issues
•
selfishness

Positive Outcome

male bonding
•
sensitivity
•
respect
•
consideration

This Essence was made up under unique circumstances on Toolbrunup Peak, the second highest peak in the Stirling Ranges. Red Helmet Orchid helps a man bond to his child or children. It helps men to be aware to allocate quality family time. Making this Essence required not only sunlight but also moonlight, thereby adding the feminine principle so as to allow bonding. It is also for anyone with unresolved father issues, which can manifest as a recurrent, lifelong rebellious attitude to authority figures — police, headmasters, bosses, etc.

Red Lily is the same flower as the Sacred Lotus in the Buddhist tradition. It is for spirituality and connection to God in a grounded and centred way, allowing a person to have a wholeness to their spirituality by also realising the need to develop and maintain a balanced physical and emotional life. It has similar properties to that of Sundew for feeling scattered, not whole, vague and split, though Sundew applies to daily life whereas Red Lily is in relation to one's spirituality. I waded thigh deep in mud through a billabong teeming with leeches, turtles and snakes to pick this flower. Such is the joy of discovery.

Red Lily

Nelumbo nucifera

Negative Condition

vague
•
disconnected
•
split
•
lack of focus
•
daydreaming

Positive Outcome

grounded
•
focused
•
living in the present
•
connection with
life and God

Red Suva Frangipani

Plumeria rubra

Negative Condition

initial grief, sadness and upset of either a relationship at rock bottom or of the death of a loved one

•

emotional upheaval, turmoil and rawness.

Positive Outcome

feeling calm and nurtured

•

inner peace and strength to cope

The Essences of this deep blood red Frangipani was made on the coast near Darwin in the Northern Territory. It is unusual in that it does not have the sweet aromatic quality of other Frangipanis but rather a very heavy, musky odour. Its common name in the Pacific is 'Bleeding Heart Frangipani'. This Essence addresses the great emotional intensity, difficulty and hardship that people can go through when a relationship is ending, close to ending or going through a very 'rocky' period.

It can also be taken for the enormous initial pain and sadness of the loss of a loved one. The person can be feeling greatly disturbed, not suicidal as in the case of Waratah, but torn apart by the event or situation. Sturt Desert Pea deals with unresolved grief from the past.

Rough Bluebell

Trichodesma zeylanicum

Negative Condition

deliberately hurtful,
manipulative, exploitive or
malicious

Positive Outcome

compassion

•

release of one's
inherent love vibration

•

sensitivity

This Essence was made in the spiritual centre of Australia in the Olgas also known as Katajuta by the Aborigines. This is an Essence to help people fully express the love vibration innate within them. Rough Bluebell is for people who are very manipulative and for those who are deliberately malicious and use people, either subtly or openly. It is different from Kangaroo Paw which is for those who hurt or ignore the needs of others in an unconscious way. This Essence can be for those who play the role of the martyr and like to have others obligated to them. They are aware of the needs of others but want love and affection for themselves and are not concerned about or unable to give it back.

She Oak

Casuarina glauca

Negative Condition

female imbalance
•
inability to conceive
for non-physical reasons

Positive Outcome

emotionally open
to conceive
•
female balance

An Essence which is very beneficial in overcoming imbalances in and bringing about a sense of wellbeing in females. It will benefit women who feel distressed about infertility. It removes those personal blocks that prevent conception. It can also be used in conjunction with Flannel Flower which will help remove karmic patterns hindering conception. The fruit of this tree is very similar in size to a woman's ovary. This Essence was made from the female tree of the species.

Silver Princess

Eucalyptus caesia

Negative Condition

aimless
•
despondent
•
feeling flat
•
lack of direction

Positive Outcome

motivation
•
direction
•
life purpose

This is another rare Eucalypt. Although widely cultivated there is only one remaining natural stand of this beautiful tree on a granite outcrop known as Boyagin Rock in the south west of Western Australia.
Of all the Eucalypts, there is none more attractive than the Silver Princess. This Essence brings about an awareness of one's life direction. Though it may not always reveal to a person their full life plan, it will aid people who are at crossroads, helping to show them what their next step is. It helps give them an understanding of that direction. This Essence is also excellent when one has reached an important goal and yet one is left feeling very flat, thinking 'is this all there is'. In this case, it gives one a glimpse or a sense of what is next and allows one to enjoy the journey whilst striving for the goal.

Slender Rice Flower

Pimelea linifolia

Negative Condition

prejudice
•
racism
•
narrow mindedness
•
comparison with others

Positive Outcome

humility
•
group harmony
•
co-operation
•
perception of beauty in others

Slender Rice Flower is for people who are racist, narrow minded and lack humility. Humanity has, through its many wars, seen the grim ramifications of these attitudes. This Essence can be used for group harmony and conflict resolution when individual egos get in the way. It allows for greater co-operation between people for the common good. This Essence has the ability to make an individual aware of the common divinity in all people.

Southern Cross

Xanthosia rotundifolia

Negative Condition

victim mentality
•
complaining
•
bitter
•
martyrs
•
poverty consciousness

Positive Outcome

personal power
•
taking responsibility
•
positiveness

This is another Essence made in the Stirling Ranges of Western Australia. It is for those people who have a tendency to feel that they are a victim, that life has been hard on them or that they have been hard done by. This Essence helps people to understand that they create all the situations that happen to them in life and that they can change their situation by changing their thoughts.

Spinifex

Triodia species

Negative Condition

sense of being a victim to illness

Positive Outcome

empowers one through
emotional understanding
of illness

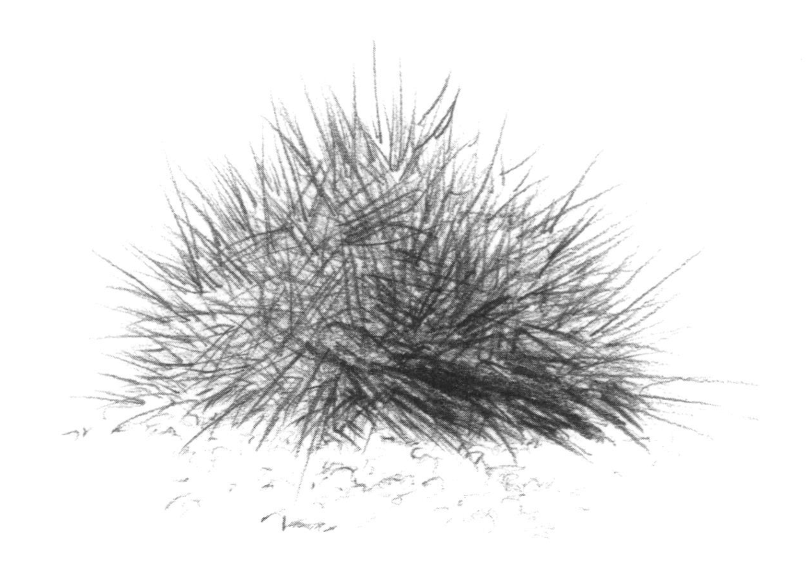

Spinifex is a native grass which prefers the arid and semi-arid areas of inland Australia. This was the first Essence made from a grass species. It is for those who have a sense of being a victim to and having no control over illnesses, especially those with persistent and recurring symptoms.

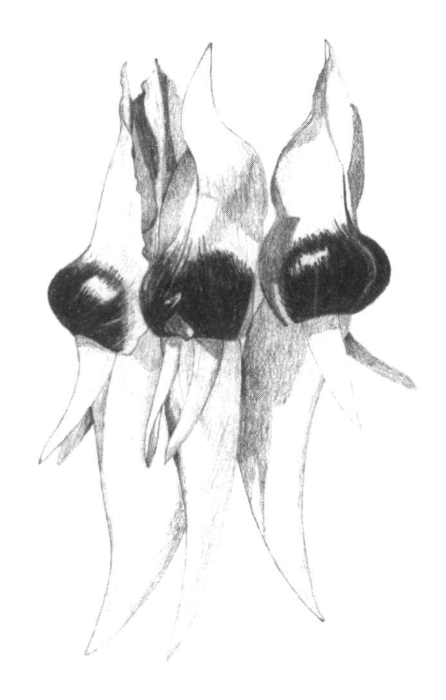

Sturt Desert Pea

Clianthus formosus

Negative Condition

emotional pain
•
deep hurt
•
sadness

Positive Outcome

letting go
•
triggers healthy grieving
•
releases deep held
grief and sadness

Sturt Desert Pea is the floral emblem of South Australia. It is for deep hurts and sorrows. I have come across at least three Aboriginal legends connecting this flower to grief and sadness. This is one of the most powerful of all the Essences and, like so many of the Bush Essences, it can help the person bring about amazing changes in their life.

Sturt Desert Rose

Gossypium sturtianum

Negative Condition

guilt
•
regret and remorse
•
low self esteem
•
easily led

Positive Outcome

courage
•
conviction
•
true to self
•
integrity

This Essence is for guilt, including sexual guilt, which can be an emotional trigger for many sexual problems. It is for following your own inner convictions and morality, helping you to follow through with what you know you have to do. If one is not true to themselves then there can often arise, as a consequence, feelings of regret or remorse. It can restore self esteem that has been damaged by past actions you may have felt guilty about.

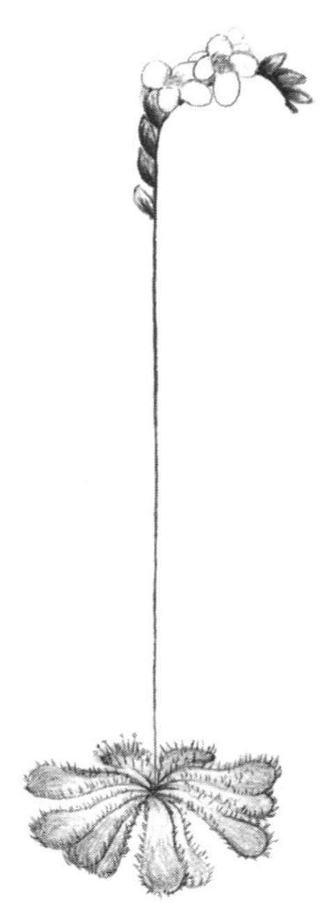

This Essence is for people who are vague and indecisive and do not pay attention to detail. For those who tend to 'split off' easily, especially when there is work to be done. This Essence will keep them focused in the present and reduces procrastination. It is for those who tend to be vague, dreamy or drawn to drugs. This carnivorous plant is found in damp, boggy areas and has a crimson, 'earth-hugging' base. It sends up a tall stem to which delicate little flowers are attached.

Sundew

Drosera spathulata

Negative Condition

vagueness
•
disconnectedness
•
split
•
indecisive
•
lack of focus
•
daydreaming

Positive Outcome

attention to detail
•
grounded
•
focused
•
living in the present

Sunshine Wattle

Acacia terminalis

Negative Condition

stuck in the past
•
expectation of
a grim future
•
struggle

Positive Outcome

optimism
•
acceptance of the
beauty and joy in the present
•
open to a bright future

For people who have had a difficult time in the past and who are stuck there. They bring their negative experiences of the past into the present. Life is seen as being grim and full of struggle. When they look at life they only see bleakness, hard times and disappointment continuing into the future. In the positive mode these people will see the beauty, joy and excitement in the present and optimistically anticipate the future.

Tall Mulla Mulla

Ptilotus exaltatus

Negative Condition

ill at ease

•

sometimes fearful of circulating and mixing with others

•

loner

•

distressed by and avoids confrontation

Positive Outcome

feeling relaxed and secure with other people

•

encourages social interaction

This is another Essence which was made up in the Olgas or Katajuta. It is a small upright annual with a long pink-purple flower head. It is for people who are not at ease being with others. They prefer their own company and enjoy being alone but miss out on the emotional growth that interaction with others can bring. On an emotional level there is not much 'circulating with people', as it feels too troublesome and uncomfortable. They do not easily mix with others. They prefer to be alone where they know their own environment and can avoid confrontation with others. They will often go to any length to keep the peace even if it means agreeing to or saying things they don't believe. They do not breathe in life deeply for they prefer holding on to the familiar rather than being open to the new.

Tall Yellow Top

Senecio magnificus

Negative Condition

alienation
•
loneliness
•
isolation

Positive Outcome

sense of belonging
•
acceptance of self and others
•
knowing that you are 'home'
•
ability to reach out

This Essence is for alienation. There is no feeling of connection or sense of belonging to family, workplace, country, self, etc. Often as a consequence of this alienation the head, or intellect, takes over from the heart. As many people have been in this state for a long time, Tall Yellow Top will often need to be used for longer periods, sometimes for up to 6-8 weeks without a break. It is important when in this state to reach out to others for support. Be patient with the results from this Essence if it appears to be a little slow in acting. The results are well worth waiting for.

Turkey Bush

Calytrix exstipulata

Negative Condition

creative block

•

disbelief in own creative ability

Positive Outcome

inspired creativity

•

creative expression

•

focus

•

renews artistic confidence

I made this Essence in Katherine Gorge, at the top end of Australia. This region contains the world's oldest known continuous artwork in the form of Aboriginal rock paintings. It is appropriate that the Essence was made here as it is for creativity. It is for both the beginner and the artist. Turkey Bush allows them to tune into their Higher Self and helps them to move through creative blocks and discouragements. This Essence brings about a desire to express and allows creativity to flow.

Waratah

Telopea speciosissima

Negative Condition

despair
•
hopelessness
•
inability to respond to a crisis

Positive Outcome

courage
•
tenacity
•
adaptability
•
strong faith
•
enhancement of survival skills

For the person who is going through the 'black night of the soul' and is in utter despair. It gives them the strength and courage to cope with their crisis and will bring their survival skills to the fore. This remedy will also enhance and amplify those skills. It is for emergencies and great challenges. This powerful remedy often only needs to be used for four or five days. The Waratah Essence was made with great assistance and guidance in profound metaphysical circumstances, from what was known to be the last flowering Waratah of the season.

Wedding Bush

Ricinocarpus pinifolius

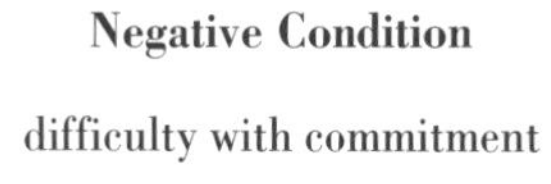

Negative Condition

difficulty with commitment

Positive Outcome

commitment to relationships
•
commitment to goals
•
dedication to life purpose

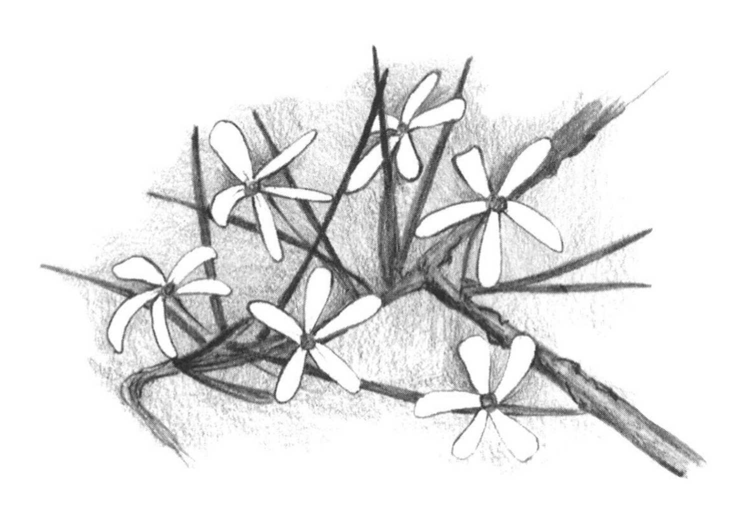

This Essence is excellent for commitment, whether in relationships, employment, the family or personal goals. It can be of great benefit for a relationship when one or both individuals are uncertain if they wish to work through the issues their partner is bringing up in them. Wedding Bush can also be used for people who flit from one relationship to another, or for when the initial attraction in the relationship diminishes.

Wild Potato Bush

Solanum quadriloculatum

Negative Condition

weighed down
•
feeling encumbered

Positive Outcome

ability to move on in life
•
freedom
•
renews enthusiasm

An excellent remedy for anyone feeling burdened or frustrated by any physical restriction or limitation with their body. This Essence brings about a sense of renewed enthusiasm, freedom and the ability to move on in life. It is especially for those who feel heavy and need to step out of the old self, but who feel it is difficult to do so.

Wisteria

Wisteria sinensis

Negative Condition

feeling uncomfortable with sex

•

closed sexually

•

macho male

Positive Outcome

sexual enjoyment

•

enhanced sensuality

•

sexual openness

•

gentleness

This Essence is for women who are uncomfortable with their sexuality. They may be unable to relax and enjoy sex, or afraid of physical intimacy and/or sensuality. Wisteria is included in the Sexuality Essence Combination for it is especially beneficial for those who have had traumatic sexual experiences. Negative beliefs around sexuality can develop from the time in the womb or from their parents attitude towards sex. The remedy works in clearing these beliefs, allowing sexual enjoyment, openness, gentleness and ease of sexual intimacy. Wisteria also allows the 'macho male' to be more aware of his softer, feminine side.

Yellow Cowslip Orchid

Caladenia flava

Negative Condition

critical
•
judgemental
•
bureaucratic
•
nit picking

Positive Outcome

humanitarian concern
•
impartiality — stepping back from emotions
•
constructive
•
a keener sense of arbitration

Yellow is the colour that symbolises the intellect and the element of Air. This orchid has a very social and gregarious nature and is commonly found growing in clusters. The element of Air is very concerned with social order, group activity and harmony. When out of balance there is excessive judgement and criticism.

Additional Flower Essences

These Essences are not included in a Stock Kit,
as they are more recent developments.

Christmas Bell

Blandfordia nobilis

Negative Condition

lack of abundance

•

sense of lack

•

poor stewardship of one's possessions

Positive Outcome

helps one to manifest their desired outcomes

•

assists one with mastery of the physical plane

Christmas Bell is an erect perennial herb which is frequently found in the Hawkesbury Sandstone country of NSW in the low open heaths or swamps. It grows up to 60cm high with a crowd of yellow tipped, red fused, tubed flowers at the top. Christmas Bell's flowering time is from late December — hence its name — up until February.

Christmas is the time of year associated with the joy of giving and receiving, not only of love, but also from the realm of the material too. This remedy assists one with mastery of the physical plane and with stewardship of one's possessions. It also helps one to manifest their desired outcomes and is extremely beneficial for anyone experiencing a sense of lack.

Monga Waratah

Telopea mongaensis

Negative Condition

neediness
•
co-dependency
•
inability to do things alone
•
disempowerment
•
addictive personality

Positive Outcome

strengthening of one's will
•
reclaiming of one's spirit
•
belief that one can break the dependency of any behaviour, substance or person
•
self empowerment

Monga Waratah a shrub up to 4 metres has a very small distribution around the moist forested areas and creeks of the Mongarlowe River near Braidwood in New South Wales. Its flower has the appearance of an open hand reaching out.

This Essence can help a person find their inner strength. It addresses the negative conditions of disempowerment; of being overly needy; of feeling not strong enough; of feeling unable to do things alone; of always needing the strength and support of others; feeling choked or stifled in situations or relationships and feeling not able or strong enough to leave. This Essence is very much addressing co-dependency as well as strengthening one's will. Consequently, it can be thought of when working with addictions. This remedy helps one to reclaim their spirit.

Sydney Rose
Boronia serrulata

Negative Condition

feeling separated, deserted, unloved or morbid

Positive Outcome

realising we are all one
•
feeling safe and at peace
•
heartfelt compassion
•
sense of unity

The first aspect of the rare Sydney Rose to strike you is its intense, beautiful colour of the purest, pure pink. Pink is symbolic of the love vibration and the healing quality of this remarkable Essence is to realise and know — on a deep heart level not merely an intellectual level — that there is no separation between us, that we are all one.

If human consciousness is going to evolve then this will need to be the one fundamental premise to be embraced and to operate from, for in so doing it will create compassion, tolerance and love for others and the willingness to help and support others. Not surprisingly then, that whilst making this Essence I kept hearing over and over this message "the crowning glory, the crowning glory, this is the crowning glory of the Bush Essences."

Companion Essences

These Essences are not included in a Stock Kit,
as they have not been made from the flowers of the plants.

Autumn Leaves

Negative Condition

difficulties in the transition of passing over from the physical plane to the spiritual world

Positive Outcome

letting go and moving on

•

increase awareness and communication with the loved ones in the spiritual world

Autumn Leaves allows one to hear, see and feel communication from the other side and be open to that guidance and communication. It also further emphasises the sense of letting go and moving on in a very profound way. The leaves themselves were collected from a sacred area, in autumn, at the exact moment of their release from the trees.
The Essence was made only from these leaves.
The work of Dr Elizabeth Kubler-Ross and other workers with the dying, all note how common and important it is for the one passing over to be aware that help and guidance are around, especially the presence of loved ones who have already died. This Essence will ease the transition of the passing over from the physical plane to the spiritual world.
Autumn Leaves is included in the Transition Essence Combination.

Green Essence

The Green Essence is made, not from the flowers, but rather the stems and leaves of traditional, fresh, green herbs, using the same method we use to make our Flower Essences. It is used to harmonise any internal yeast, mould and parasites to the same vibration as one's body. It should be taken orally for a minimum two week period, five drops 3 times a day, five minutes before meals.

Green Essence can also be used topically on the skin. Place seven drops of Green Essence in a dessert bowl of water, splash on the affected area and allow to dry. Do this morning and night for two weeks. You will need to make a fresh batch every two days. You can also douche if necessary with Green Essence. This is most effectively done morning and night for a two week period. We recommend not using Green Essence externally at the same time as it is taken internally.

Negative Condition

emotional distress associated
with intestinal and skin disorders

Positive Outcome

harmonises the vibration
of any yeast, mould or parasite
to one's own vibration

•

purifying

Lichen

Parmelia s. lat.

Negative Condition

not knowing to look for
and move into the Light when
passing over

•

earth bound in the astral plane

Positive Outcome

eases one's transition into
the Light

•

assists separation between the
physical and the etheric bodies

•

releases earth bound energies

Lichen helps an individual to be aware of, look for and go to the Light at the moment of physical death. The alternative to the soul going through to the Light is to stay earth bound in the astral plane — what we commonly refer to as "a ghost". There is a great deal of darkness operating on the astral plane and it is certainly a level that the soul would be well advised to move through quickly.

A violent or sudden death can also result in the increased likelihood of the Spirit staying earthbound and the spraying of Lichen from an atomiser bottle would be of great benefit for those souls, helping them to see and go to the Light. Even in cases where there is an unexpected sudden death, eg. a car accident, the individual who dies in such an experience, is fully aware at the level of their Higher Self, of what is about to happen and that they are going to pass over. Two weeks before such an event the etheric body starts to disengage and unravel from the physical body. Lichen assists the etheric and the physical bodies to separate in preparation for passing over.

Lichen is contained in the Transition Essence Combination. The latter can be taken by people who are in the process of passing over or else going through major changes in their life such as changing career, moving house, etc. In these latter circumstances one can rest assured that the Lichen in this Combination would definitely not lead to their etheric body separating from their physical body!

THE AUSTRALIAN BUSH FLOWER ESSENCE SOCIETY

The Society has been formed to provide you with the most up to date information on the Flower Essences. There is a minimal annual subscription fee for which members receive four newsletters per year containing updates on Essences, details of workshops and many special offers. It will also allow you a forum, through the publication of case histories, to share your knowledge and experience of Flower Essences.

We are always happy to receive any case histories or testimonials — Your contributions are greatly valued.

INFORMATION

For further information on the Society or our ever evolving and expanding range of products please contact our office or website.

Bush Biotherapies Pty Ltd trading as Australian Bush Flower Essences
45 Booralie Road
Terrey Hills NSW 2084
Australia

Telephone: (02) 9450 1388 International: 61+2 9450 1388
Facsimile: (02) 9450 2866 International: 61+2 9450 2866
Email: info@ausflowers.com.au
Website: www.ausflowers.com.au

WHITE LIGHT ESSENCES RANGE

The White Light Essences have been brought through by Spirit to help us invoke and access the realm of Nature and Spirit within ourselves, so as to more fully explore and understand our spirituality and fulfil our highest potential.

In much Love, Light and Respect,
Ian White

White Light Essence Pyramid Pack

The White Light Essence pyramid pack has been carefully developed to embrace and protect the beauty and potency of these wonderful Essences.
The White Light Essence pyramid pack contains all 7 spiritual stock Essences, Ian's new book and the White Light CD.

The Book "White Light Essences"

Ian White's new book "White Light Essences", takes you on a magical journey to some of the worlds most sacred sites where you will experience the making of these vibrational Essences. These breathtaking panoramas have been exquisitely captured in the colour photographs which accompany the text. The book will lead you through each Essence's unique spiritual and soul healing qualities which can be utilised in both personal and practitioner application.

The CD "White Light"

Sound [pure vibration], is the force inherent in all things, it has a powerful effect on the cellular structure of human beings and a very profound effect on our psyche and soul. In esoteric numerology each person's master number corresponds with a specific colour. Also associated with each colour is a musical composition. The White Light CD contains these 8 specific musical masterpieces, beautifully recorded, that when heard, will help bring into balance anyone whose master number corresponds to that particular colour.

Individual Essence Pyramid Packs

Stock Essences for each of the individual White Light Essences are available. They come in the individual pyramid packs carefully developed to embrace and protect the beauty and potency of these wonderful Essences.

Australian Bush Flower Essences
publications

Ian has 2 other publications: • Australian Bush Flower Essences • Bush Flower Healing

Australian Bush Flower Essences

In AUSTRALIAN BUSH FLOWER ESSENCES Ian gives an informative and personal picture of the first fifty Bush Flower Essences which includes the unique story behind each Essence and its use in all areas of healing. Beautifully illustrated with photos of the individual flowers, this book also covers chapters on: · History and philosophy of Flower Essences · How Flower Essences work · How to make, prepare and take an Essence · Using the Essences with other modalities such as Numerology, Kinesiology and Age Regression · Sexuality and the Bush Essences · Meditation and the Bush Essences · An index of illnesses and their treatment.

This comprehensive text is designed to allow anyone, practitioner or novice to feel competent and confident using the Australian Bush Flower Essences to bring about health, harmony and well being. A review of the book: *"For those who want a warm, personal and concise reference book – beautifully illustrated, this book is yours."* – AS REVIEWED BY: THE AUSTRALIAN TRADITIONAL MEDICINE SOCIETY

Bush Flower Healing

The long awaited companion volume to Ian White's bestselling AUSTRALIAN BUSH FLOWER ESSENCES, first published in 1991 and still the authoritative book in the field. This second book, BUSH FLOWER HEALING, covers the 12 Essences that were developed after his first book was published. This text is also fully illustrated and contains stunning photos of not only the new Bush Essence flowers, but also landscapes of the areas where they grow. One of the most valuable aspects of this book is the extensive repertory of emotional, mental and spiritual conditions. This index is a wonderful reference point when researching or selecting a Bush Essence. Other topics covered include:

· Important new research on the first 50 Bush Essences · How to prepare and take the Essences · Formulas for Combination Essences · The Companion Essences · Emotional patterns and balance in pregnancy and labour · Goal setting and goal achieving · Astrology, health and the Bush Essences · Bush Essences and the related subtle bodies

insight flower cards

The Flower Insight Cards were first developed in 1997 after numerous requests from both practitioners and patients to see the flowers in all their glory! Beautifully photographed and in full colour, each card reflects the vibrancy and potency of each Essence, whilst also opening up many new ways of healing with the Australian Bush Flower Essences. These cards will also help you to deeply understand the clues nature has given to the healing qualities of each flower by its shape and colour – what ancient healers termed the Doctrine of Signatures.
Available in a pack 62 cards

correspondence course

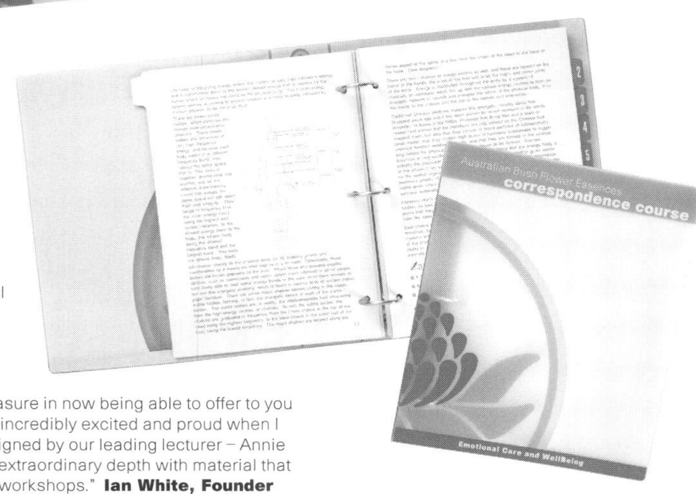

The Australian Bush Flower Essences' Correspondence Course has been designed and written by Annie Meredith, a Practitioner with over 20 years experience. She is a senior lecturer with both Australian Bush Flower Essences and the Australian College of Natural Therapies in Brisbane where she lectures in Australian Bush Flower Essences, Traditional Chinese Medicine and Vibrational Medicine.

"After 15 years of teaching the Australian Bush Flower Essences' Workshops, I have great pleasure in now being able to offer to you our brand new Correspondence Course. I was incredibly excited and proud when I read this course, it is brilliantly written and designed by our leading lecturer – Annie Meredith. It explores the Bush Essences at an extraordinary depth with material that has never been presented before in any of our workshops." **Ian White, Founder**

Since obtaining his Bachelor of Science from the University of New South Wales and graduating from the NSW College of Natural Therapies, Ian White has been practising successfully as a Naturopath and Homoeopath for 25 years. He is the founder of the Australian Bush Flower Essences and a fifth generation Australian herbalist. Both his grandmother and great grandmother were early pioneers in discovering the medicinal properties of Australian plants and as a boy Ian spent a great deal of time with his grandmother in the bush learning from her.

Ian has spent the last 18 years travelling extensively throughout Australia researching the healing qualities of the Australian flora.

He is the author of four major books and contributes articles to well known Australian and International publications. He also regularly conducts seminars on the Australian Bush Flower Essences throughout the world.